WHAT TIME IS IT, JEANNE-MARIE?

Françoise

WHAT TIME IS IT JEANNE-MARIE?

Charles Scribner's Sons
New York

Printed in the United States of America
L.C.C.C. No. 63-21302
SBN 684-12457-2
1 13 15 17 19 RD/C 20 18 16 14 12 10 8

Get up, get up, Jeanne-Marie.
The weather is fine. The sun shines.
It is

7 o'clock

Jeanne-Marie has breakfast.
Then her father takes her to school.
Patapon does not go to school. She stays
at home. It is

Jeanne-Marie likes her school and all her friends,
Lisette and Pierrot,
Babette and Toto, and Titine.

9 o'clock

Lisette
Pierrot
Babette
Toto
Titine

When the teacher asks a question, Jeanne-Marie raises her hand and says, "I know."
Time goes by quickly.
It is 10 o'clock, 11 o'clock, eleven-thirty.

Class is over!

Every day Jeanne-Marie has soup for lunch
with her aunt and uncle.
Bon appétit, Jeanne-Marie!
It is

After lunch school begins again. Pierrot rings the bell. Ding . . . Ding . . . Dong. It is

2 o'clock

Jeanne-Marie likes drawing class.
She works very hard.
She draws a picture of Patapon. It is

quarter to 4

After school
Jeanne-Marie meets her friend Jean-Pierre.
Jeanne-Marie goes wading.
Jean-Pierre takes Patapon
out in the boat.
It is

5 o'clock

What is there for dinner?
Fish from the brook and strawberries
from the garden.
It is

quarter past 6

After supper
Jeanne-Marie helps her grandmother.
It is

8:30

Late at night everybody is asleep.
Mother, Father, Grandmother,
Jeanne-Marie, Patapon.
Only the moon does not sleep.
It is

La lune rit

Bonne nuit

!

FRENCH WORDS USED IN THIS STORY

At noontime Jeanne-Marie has lunch with her aunt and uncle. The word for *noon* in French is *midi.*

To wish someone a pleasant meal, the French say *bon appétit!*

Late at night when everyone is asleep, the hands of the clock point to twelve. *Midnight* in French is *minuit.*

The last lines of this picture story—*La lune rit, bonne nuit*—mean *The moon is smiling, good night.*